Baby Jesus

by Alison Hedger

The traditional Biblical Nativity story
with seven new songs written for young children.
Simple percussion parts are included.

Duration approx. 25 mins.

For Pre-school children,
Key Stage 1 and Special Education Units.

TEACHER'S BOOK
Complete with script, songs with simple piano accompaniment,
chord symbols and optional percussion.

MUSIC

Introduction *metallophone/chimes*
Song 1. There Was A Girl Called Mary
Song 2. Have You Any Room At The Inn? *woodblock*
Musical Interlude
Song 3. Shepherds Were Looking After Baby Lambs
Musical Interlude *triangle*
Song 4. A Special Star *triangle*
Song 5. Three Wise Men Had Travelled Far
Song 6. Baby Jesus *metallophone/chimes*
Song 7. Sing A Little Song Of Happiness *clapping/percussion*

A matching tape cassette of the music for rehearsals and performances is available,
Order No. GA10982, with narration and singing included on side A and omitted on side B.

© Copyright 1995 Golden Apple Productions
A division of Chester Music Limited
8/9 Frith Street, London W1V 5TZ

Order No. GA10981
ISBN 0-7119-5020-2

BABY JESUS was written as a follow-up to GOLD, FRANKINCENSE AND MYRRH. The songs are simple yet colourful and the piano part has been kept easy enough for most school pianists to cope with.

Percussion parts have been added. These will provide interest to the music and also give a great sense of achievement to the players. Wrong notes or misplaced percussion are not a problem, it is the challenge of taking part which counts.

The lyrics are uncluttered and so are manageable by very young children and those with learning difficulties.

The story may be read by an adult or given to fluent readers. The A side of the companion tape (GA10982) includes the story. The B side has just the musical accompaniment so that children can happily sing along either in class or to an audience.

No acting ideas or stage directions are given, as every situation is different. BABY JESUS provides a versatile work into which adults can incorporate their own ideas. How much acting or mime is included will be dictated by circumstances.

Thank you for sharing BABY JESUS with me.

With best wishes,

Alison Hedger

INTRODUCTION

metallophone/chimes

repeat the music as necessary

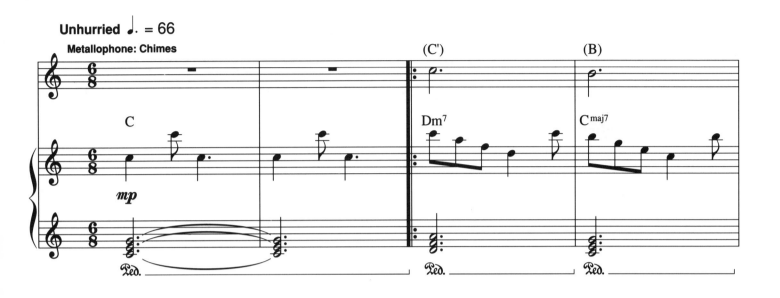

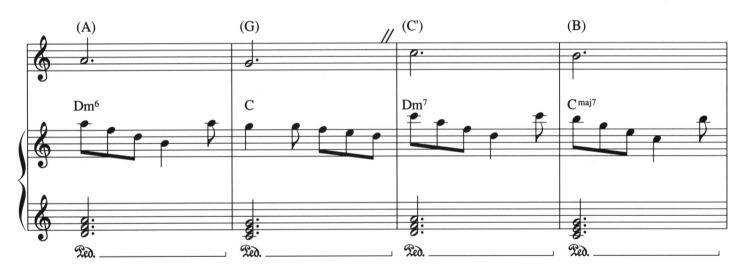

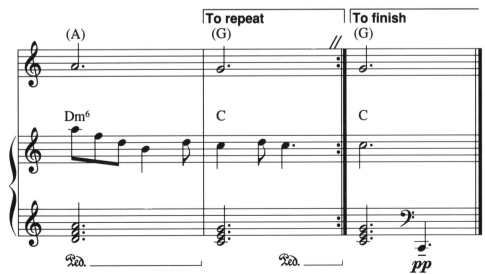

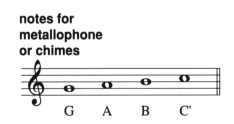

notes for metallophone or chimes

A long time ago in a far away country there lived a girl called Mary. She was to be married to a man called Joseph.

♪ 1. There was a girl called Mary, Mary, Mary.
   There was a girl called Mary.
   Mary was her name.

2. There was a man called Joseph, Joseph, Joseph.
   There was a man called Joseph.
   Joseph was his name.

3. And they were to be married, married, married.
   And they were to be married,
   And have a family.

THERE WAS A GIRL CALLED MARY

One day an angel visited Mary and told her that she was to have a very special baby boy. He was to be called Jesus and would be the Son of God.

Now at this time, the ruler of the land ordered everyone to go to their home town to be counted. This meant that Joseph and Mary had to travel to the town of Bethlehem.

♪ 5. They went together to Bethlehem, Bethlehem, Bethlehem.
   They went together to Bethlehem.
   To Bethlehem they went.

6. So Mary rode a donkey, donkey, donkey.
   So Mary rode a donkey
   With Joseph by her side.

7. For Mary was having a baby, baby, baby.
   For Mary was having a baby,
   And soon he would be born.

(music continues for Mary and Joseph to travel to)

THERE WAS A GIRL CALLED MARY

(the key has changed from E minor to F major)

Play music an octave higher as many times as necessary, for Mary and Joseph to travel to.

Lots of other families had also arrived in Bethlehem and the town was very crowded. Every hotel, inn and boarding house was full. There were no empty rooms for Joseph and Mary. They knocked upon every door hoping that at last someone would have a spare room.

♪ Have you any room at the inn?
Have you any room at the inn?
We've been here and we've been there,
We've been asking everywhere.
Have you any room at the inn?

(repeat song as many times as necessary)

SONG TWO # HAVE YOU ANY ROOM AT THE INN?

woodblock

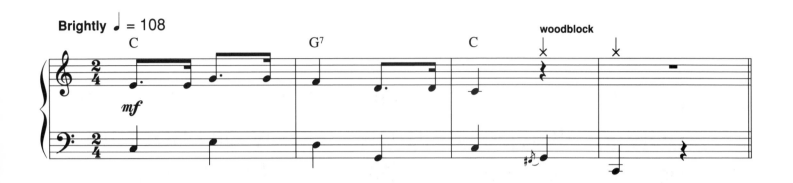

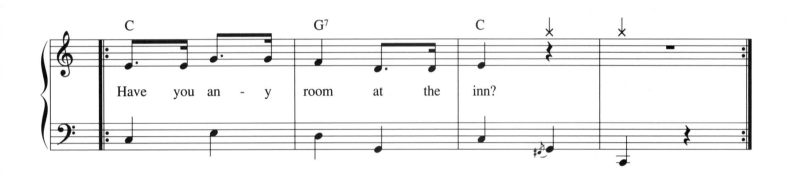

Have   you an – y   room   at   the   inn?

We've   been   here   and   we've   been there,   we've   been ask – ing   ev – 'ry - where.

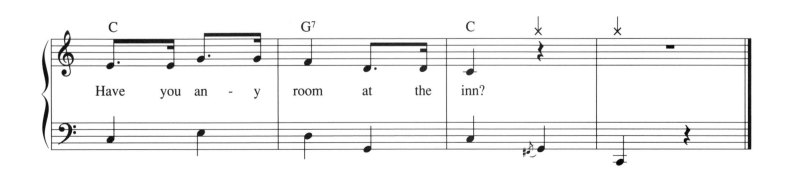

Have   you   an – y   room   at   the   inn?

Joseph was just about to give up in despair when a friendly inn-keeper said that if they did not mind sharing with his animals, they could rest for the night in his stable. Joseph gladly accepted as Mary was very tired.

That night baby Jesus was born in the stable.

Mary laid the new baby in the manger full of hay. She had no other bed for him. Joseph kept watch over his family. Mary rested and the baby slept peacefully.

(musical interlude for Mary and Joseph to look at and enjoy their baby)

MUSICAL INTERLUDE

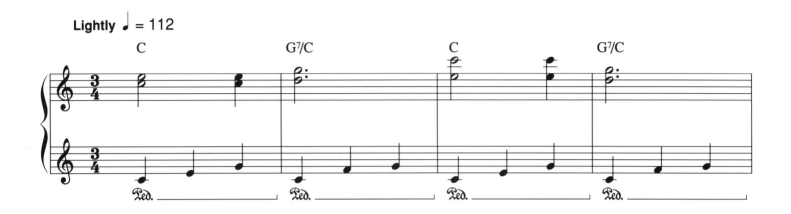

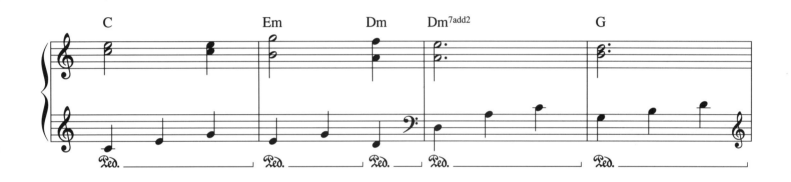

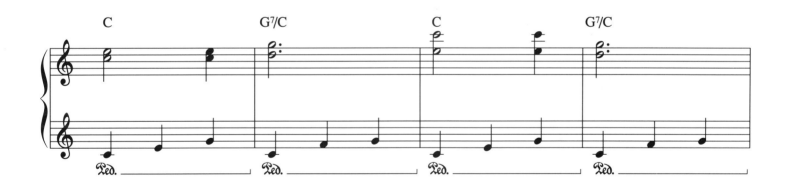

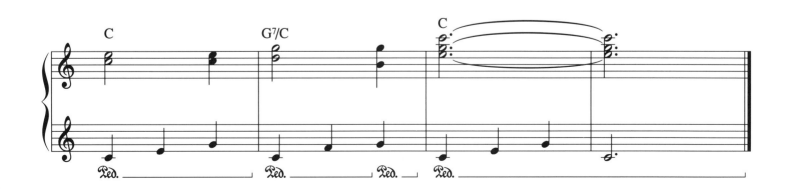

On a hillside outside Bethlehem there were some shepherds looking after their sheep. The night was dark and still. All of a sudden something very strange happened. The night sky lit up with hundreds of angels singing and praising God. This was a wondrous sight!

♪ 1.　Shepherds were looking after baby lambs,
　　　　baby lambs.
　　　Shepherds were looking after baby lambs
　　　In the dark, dark night.

2.　Then all the shepherds heard the angels' song,
　　　angels' song.
　　Then all the shepherds heard the angels' song
　　As the sky was filled with light.

3.　Angels sang with voices bright.
　　Music echoed in the night.
　　Angels sang with voices clear,
　　"Seek the Lord for He is near."

4.　Shepherds were looking after baby lambs,
　　　baby lambs.
　　Shepherds were looking after baby lambs
　　When they saw the wondrous sight!

CODA　Hundreds and hundreds and hundreds and
　　　　hundreds of angels!

SONG THREE SHEPHERDS WERE LOOKING AFTER BABY LAMBS

Steadily ♩ = 100

1. Shep - herds were look - ing af - ter
2. Then all the shep - herds heard the

ba - by lambs, ba - by lambs. Shep - herds were look - ing af - ter
an - gels' song, an - gels' song. Then all the shep - herds heard the

ba - by lambs in the dark,__ dark__ night.
an - gels' song as the sky was filled with light.

3. An - gels sang with voi - ces bright. Mu - sic ech - oed

in the night. An - gels sang with voi - ces clear,

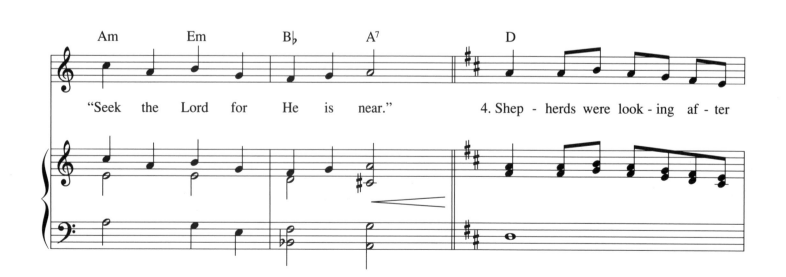

"Seek the Lord for He is near." 4. Shep - herds were look - ing af - ter

ba - by lambs,   ba - by lambs.   Shep - herds were look - ing af - ter

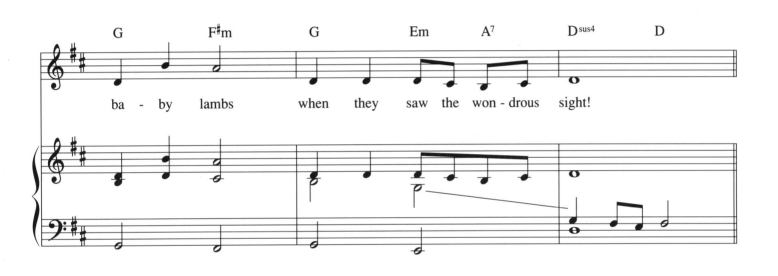

ba - by lambs   when they   saw the won - drous sight!

CODA

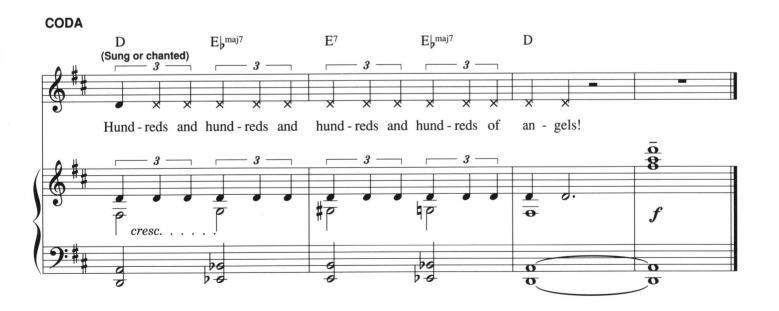

Hund - reds and hund - reds and   hund - reds and hund - reds of   an - gels!

The shepherds hurried down from the hillside into the town to find the newly born baby. Up in the sky a new star shone brightly and its twinkling light showed the shepherds where Baby Jesus was. It shone right over the stable.

(music for shepherds to enter the stable)

MUSICAL INTERLUDE

triangle

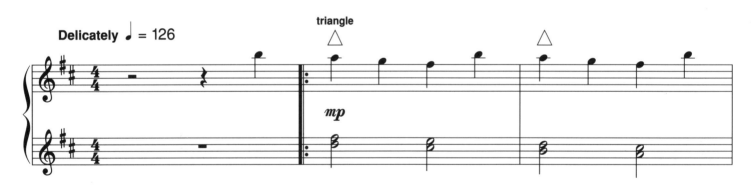

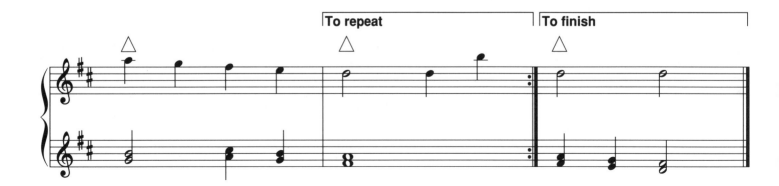

Three wise men had also seen the new star and knew that it meant something very special. A king had been born. They set off to search for him.

The star showed them the way.

 1.   A special star shone bright that night
To show the way to Jesus.
Its twinkling light was very bright
And showed the way to Jesus.

2.   The three wise men they followed that star,
Followed that star, followed that star.
The three wise men they followed that star
All the way to Jesus.

(music continues as wise men enter the stable)

A SPECIAL STAR

triangle

The chords shown have been simplified.

The wise men brought gifts with them of gold, frankincense and myrrh for the baby king.

They laid their gifts before the manger and Mary thanked them for their kindness.

♪ 1. Three wise men had travelled far
Following the brightest star.
Bringing gifts of things quite rare,
For the baby king to share.

(solo) 2. I'm a wise man. This I bring,
Gold so precious for the king.
Mine's a gift which is quite rare,
For the baby king to share.

(solo) 3. I'm a wise man. This I bring,
Frankincense for the little king.
Mine's a gift which is quite rare,
For the baby king to share.

(solo) 4. I'm a wise man. This I bring,
Myrrh so fragrant for the king.
Mine's a gift which is quite rare,
For the baby king to share.

(repeat) 1. Three wise men had travelled far . . . etc.

(the next song follows straight on)

SONG FIVE THREE WISE MEN HAD TRAVELLED FAR

possible solo parts for the wise men

(these may be spoken over the music if more appropriate)

All: 1. Three wise men had tra - velled far   fol - low - ing the bright - est star.
Solo: 2. I'm a wise man this I bring,   gold so pre - cious for the king.
Solo: 3. I'm a wise man this I bring,   fran - kin - cense for the lit - tle king.
Solo: 4. I'm a wise man this I bring,   myrrh so fra - grant for the king.

Bring - ing gifts of things quite rare,   for the ba - by king to share.
Mine's a gift which is quite rare,   for the ba - by king to share.

To finish repeat verse 1

Baby Jesus lying there
Sleeping in the manger.
Joseph's looking after him
Keeping him from danger.

Mary his mother meek and mild
Loving her little baby child.
Shepherds and wise men bend their knee,
Everyone is happy.

Baby Jesus lying there
Sleeping in the manger.
Joseph's looking after him
Keeping him from danger.

(music continues to allow for any movement required)

SONG SIX

BABY JESUS
metallophone/chimes

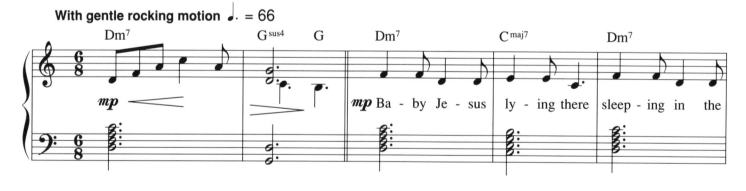

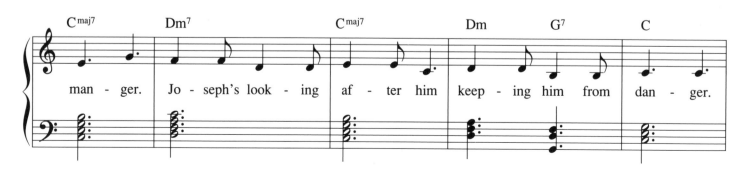

Ostinato begins and continues to finish of piano

Ma - ry his moth - er meek and mild lov - ing her lit - tle ba - by child. Shep - herds and wise men bend their knee, ev - ery - one is hap - py. Ba - by Je - sus ly - ing there sleep - ing in the man - ger. Jo - seph's look - ing af - ter him keep - ing him from dan - ger.

Ostinato: chimes/metallophone

A   G

Although Baby Jesus was born a very long time ago, we still celebrate his birthday. We call it Christmas. It is a time of great happiness, of giving and sharing. A time to be especially kind and thoughtful.

(break here for a prayer if required)

Let's make a joyful noise and celebrate Christmas together. Everyone, please join in with us.

♪ 1. Sing a little song of happiness, *(three times)*
   This happy Christmas time. Oh!

2. Sing a little song of cheerfulness, *(three times)*
   This cheerful Christmas time. Oh!

3. Sing a little song of joyfulness, *(three times)*
   This joyful Christmas time. Oh!

4. Clap your hands together, 1,2,3, *(three times)*
   This happy Christmas time. Oh!

5. Join your hands together, make a friend, *(three times)*
   This happy Christmas time. Oh!

6. La, la, la, la, la, etc . . .
   This happy Christmas time.

SING A LITTLE SONG OF HAPPINESS

clapping/use of percussion as desired

(audience link hands for verse 5)

See opposite page for words to v. 4,5,6.

25

BABY JESUS

this page is for your personalised production notes:
cast, costumes, props, staging etc.

10/95 (22740)

Printed and bound in Great Britain by
Caligraving Limited Thetford Norfolk